The Enormous Turnip

Autumn Publishing

Once upon a time, an old man planted some turnip seeds.

Then, a week went by. Some tiny turnips were peeping through. The old man could see three turnips, but one was different.

Whee!

That turnip s**ee**ms enormous!

ee

Can you spot these 5 items somewhere in the scene?

Place the stickers from your sticker sheet here as you find each one.

s**ee**ds

bee

tr**ee**

sh**ee**p

f**ee**t

Good job

ee

3

The other little turnips grew r**oo**ts and sh**oo**ts, but the enormous turnip s**oo**n looked fully grown.

Focus on the **oo** sound (as in r**oo**ts) as you read.

I think it'll reach the m**oo**n s**oo**n.

After a storm, the turnip grew even more enormous. It started to squash the sweetcorn.

Focus on the **or** sound (as in h**or**se) as you read.

One morning, the old man went to look for his garden fork to dig up the turnip.

It's now or never!

or

Can you spot these 5 items somewhere in the scene?

Place the stickers from your sticker sheet here as you find each one.

storm

horse

fork

door

sweetcorn

Nice

work

or

7

The old man heaved as he struggled with the enormous, **pur**ple t**ur**nip.

Suddenly, he felt a b**ur**ning pain in his back. He t**ur**ned to his wife and groaned.

I need a n**ur**se!

Focus on the **ur** sound (as in t**ur**nip) as you read.

8